Piano · Vocal · Guitar

# christina aguiler

*ed*

**Wise Publications**
PART OF THE MUSIC SALES GROUP
London/New York/Paris/Sydney/Copenhagen/Berlin/Madrid/Tokyo

Published by:
Wise Publications

Exclusive Distributors:
Music Sales Limited
8/9 Frith Street, London W1D 3JB, England
Music Sales Pty Limited
120 Rothschild Avenue, Rosebury, NSW 2018, Australia

Order No. AM977361
ISBN: 1-84449-059-9

Printed in the United States of America

**www.musicsales.com**

# CAN'T HOLD US DOWN

Words and Music by CHRISTINA AGUILERA,
MATT MORRIS and SCOTT STORCH

1. what, am I not s'posed to ___ have an o-pin-ion? Should I keep qui-et just be - cause I'm a wom-an?
2. what, am I not s'posed to ___ say what I'm say-ing? Are you of-fend-ed with the ___ mes-sage I'm bring-ing?

1. Call me a bitch 'cause I speak what's on my mind. Guess it's eas-i-er for you to swal-low if I sat and ___ smiled.
2. Call me what-ev-er, 'cause your words don't mean a thing. Guess you ain't e-ven a man e-nough to han-dle what I ___ sing.

# WALK AWAY

Words and Music by CHRISTINA AGUILERA,
MATT MORRIS and SCOTT STORCH

I keep go-ing right back to the one __ thing that I __ need, oh. __ I can't mend __ this torn state I'm in, __ get-ting

noth-ing in re-turn. What did I do to de-serve __ the pain of this __ slow burn? And ev-'ry-where I turn, __

I keep go-ing right back to the one __ thing that I __ need... __ to

walk a-way __ from, yeah. __

(I need to get a-way from ya, need to walk a-way from ya.)

# FIGHTER

Words and Music by CHRISTINA AGUILERA
and SCOTT STORCH

Moderately

*Spoken:* After all you put me through, you'd think I'd despise you. But in the end, I wanna thank you, 'cause you

made me that much stronger. Well, I

thought I knew you, think-ing that you were true. Guess I,
saw it com-ing, all of your back-stab-bing, just so

I could-n't trust; called your bluff, time is up, 'cause I've had e-nough. You were
you could cash in on a good thing be-fore I'd re-al-ize your game. I heard

# INFATUATION

Words and Music by CHRISTINA AGUILERA,
MATT MORRIS and SCOTT STORCH

**Moderately, with a Latin feel**

*Lead Vocal ad lib.*

He comes— from a for-eign place,— an is - land— far a - way.—

In - trigues— me with ev - ery move— till I'm breath-less, I'm help-less, can't keep my cool.—

*Original key: A♭ minor. This edition has been transposed down one half-step to be more playable.*

Cm        D7        Gm

"Ay, Ma-ma,__ you seem to for-get, I'm not in love yet; sweet talk__don't win__ me o - ver."
"Ay, Ma-ma,__ you seem to for-get, I nev-er will let   a   man__ con-trol__my e -mo- tions."

Cm7        D7

But I re - al - ize__ big brown eyes can hyp - no - tize__ when he__ says, __)
But when he smiles,__ I feel   like a lit-tle   child,__ and when he__ says, __)

Gm        Cm        D7

"I __ am full__ blood Bo - ri - cua"     reads the tat-oo on __ his arm. __

Gm        Cm        D7

He tells__ me, "Ma-mi, I need ya,"     and my heart-beat pumps__ so strong. __

# LOVING ME 4 ME

Words and Music by CHRISTINA AGUILERA,
MATT MORRIS and SCOTT STORCH

**Slowly**

People ask__ if I'm__ in__ love__
Now, peo - ple ask__ why I'm__ in__ love

___ with__ you,__ 'cause I'm sit - ting here__ with your pic - ture__ and
___ with__ you.__ Well, let me start__ by say - ing you got my heart__ by just

smil - ing to__ my - self.__ I'm kind - a lost__ in my own__ thoughts__
be - ing who__ you are.__ And what we got__ is be - tween_ me

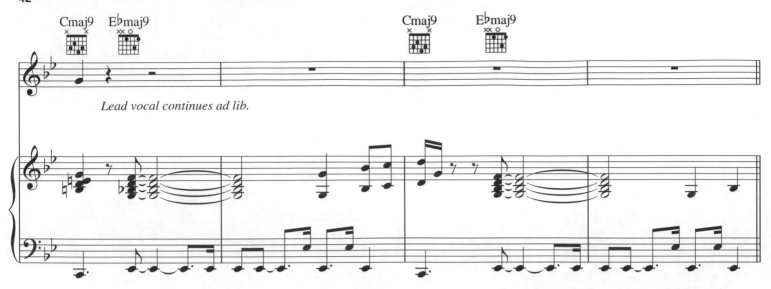

*Lead vocal continues ad lib.*

Rap: *(See Rap lyrics)*

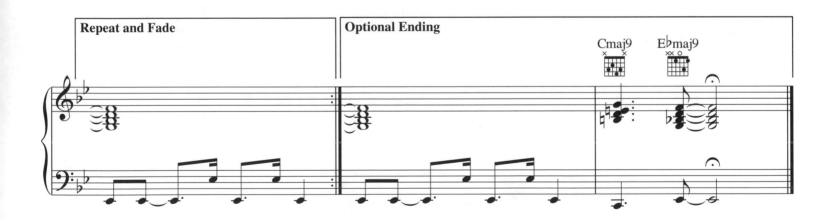

**Repeat and Fade**

**Optional Ending**

*Rap Lyrics*

Stripped of all make-up,
No need for fancy clothes;
No cover ups, no push ups;
With him, I don't have to put on a show.

He loves every freckle, every curve,
Every inch of my skin,
Fulfilling me entirely,
Taking all of me in.

He's real, he's honesty,
He's loving me 4 me.
Yeah.

# IMPOSSIBLE

Words and Music
by ALICIA KEYS

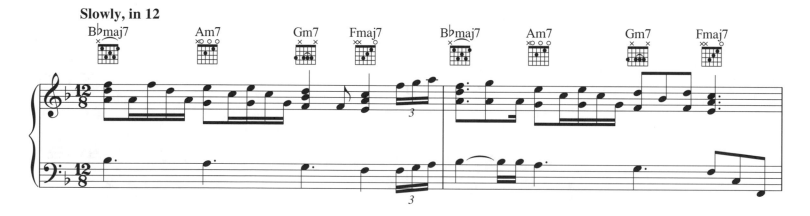

Oh, oh, oh, oh. Oh, oh, oh, oh.

# UNDERAPPRECIATED

Words and Music by CHRISTINA AGUILERA,
MATT MORRIS and SCOTT STORCH

# BEAUTIFUL

Words and Music by
LINDA PERRY

**Moderately slow**

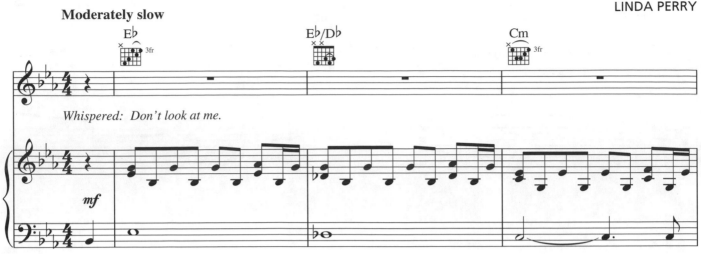

*Whispered: Don't look at me.*

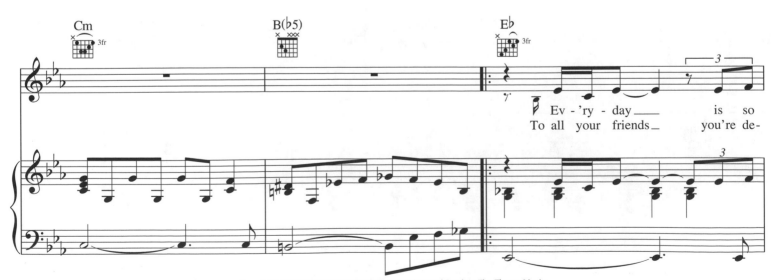

Ev-'ry-day____ is so
To all your friends____ you're de-

# MAKE OVER

Words and Music by CHRISTINA AGUILERA
and LINDA PERRY

I can't be-lieve what you did to me.
Feel-ing con-fined, like I'm be-ing force fed;

Down on my knees, and I need to break free. All these years,
my vi-sion's blur-ry, and I'm lost in re-grets. It's o - ver - load,

you vi-o-lat-ed me.
and I'm out of con-trol.

You wan-na ___ break me ___ down. ___

# CRUZ

Words and Music by CHRISTINA AGUILERA
and LINDA PERRY

**Moderately slow**

I'm leav-ing_ to-day;___ liv-ing it, leav-ing it to change.____

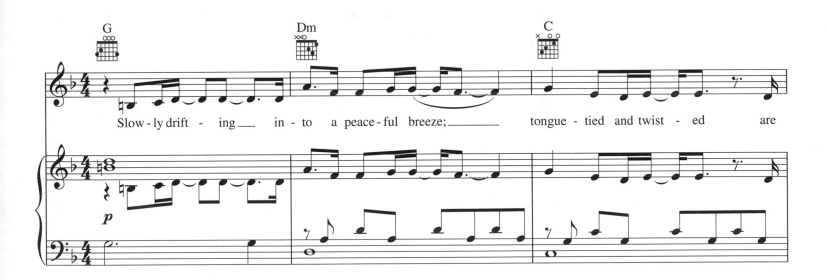

Slow-ly drift-ing___ in-to a peace-ful breeze;_____ tongue-tied and twist-ed are

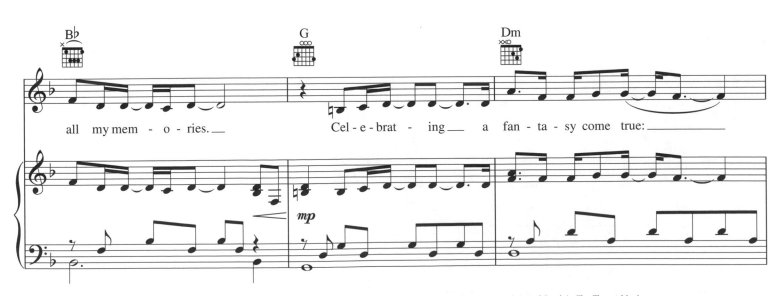

all my mem-o-ries.___ Cel-e-brat-ing___ a fan-ta-sy come true:_____

# SOAR

Words and Music by CHRISTINA AGUILERA,
ROB HOFFMAN and HEATHER HOLLEY

When they push, when they pull, tell me, can you hold on?
The boy who wonders, is he good enough for them,

When they say you should change, can you lift your head high and stay strong?
keeps try'n' to please 'em all but he just never seems to fit in.

Will you give up, give in; when your heart's crying out that it's wrong?
Then there's the girl who thinks she'll never ever be good enough for him;

# GET MINE, GET YOURS

Words and Music by CHRISTINA AGUILERA, DAVID SIEGEL,
STEVE MORALES and BALEWA MUHAMMAD

# DIRRTY

Words and Music by CHRISTINA AGUILERA,
DANA STINSON, JASPER CAMERON,
BALEWA MUHAMMAD and REGGIE NOBLE

**Heavy beat**

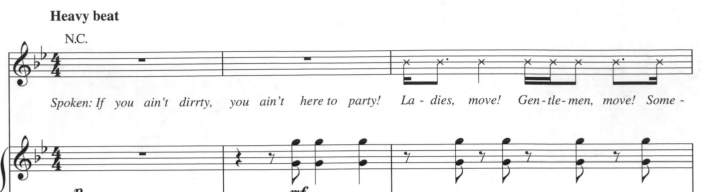

Spoken: If you ain't dirrty, you ain't here to party! La - dies, move! Gen - tle - men, move! Some -

bod - y ring the a - larm, a fire in the room! Ring the a - larm... and I'm throw - in' el - bows.

Ring the a - larm... and I'm throw - in' el - bows. Ring the a - larm... and I'm throw - in' el - bows.

Ring the a - larm... *and I'm throw-in' el - bows.* *Uhh... let me loose.*

Ooh, I'm o - ver - due; gim - me some room, com - in' through.
Ah, heat is up. La - dies fel - las, drop your cups.

Paid my dues; I'm in the mood. Me and my girls come to shake the room.
Bod - ies packed front to back. Move your ass, I like that.

D. J.'s spin - nin', show your hands. Let's get dirr - ty, that's my jam. I
Tight hip - hug - gers, low for sho'. Shake a lit - tle some - thin' on the flo'. I

bod - y. Danc-in' get-tin' just a lit-tle naugh-ty. Wan-na get dirr-ty.

**1** N.C. It's a - bout time for my ar - ri - val.

**2** N.C. It's a - bout time for my ar - ri - val. *Uhh, what?*

*Additional Lyrics*

**Rap:** Hot damn! Got the jam, like a summer show.
I keep my pawn lookin' like a crash dummy drove.
My gear look like the bait got my money froze.
But there are presidents I pimp like Teddy Ro'.
Got the one that excites ya deepest,
At the media shine, I'm shinin' with both of the sleeves up.
Yo Christina, what happened here?
My black, live and in color, like Rodman hair.

The club is packed, the bar is filled, they're waitin' for
Sister to act like Lauren Hill. Frankly,
It's so black, no bargain deals, I'll drop a
Four-wheel drive with foreign wheels. Throw it up!
Bet you this is Brick City, you heard o' that.
We're blessed and hung low, like Bernie Mack.
Dogs, let 'em out; women, let 'em in.
It's like I'm O.D.B., that what they're thinkin'.

# THE VOICE WITHIN

Words and Music by CHRISTINA AGUILERA
and GLEN BALLARD

# I'M OK

Words and Music by CHRISTINA AGUILERA
and LINDA PERRY

# KEEP ON SINGIN' MY SONG

Words and Music by CHRISTINA AGUILERA
and SCOTT STORCH